MASTERING SOFTWARE TESTING: A BEGINNER TO EXPERT GUIDE

DEVARSH SHAH

Made with ♥ on the Notion Press Platform
www.notionpress.com

To every aspiring QA engineer who, when faced with a failure or a setback, chose to ask, "Why did this fail?" instead of simply accepting it and moving on this journey is yours as much as it is mine. It's easy to be discouraged when things don't go according to plan, but it's your curiosity, your determination to dig deeper and seek understanding, that separates you from those who merely go through the motions. It's the critical thinking, the persistence to not just find problems but to solve them, that shapes you into a true expert in your field. So, here's to the questioners, the ones who refuse to settle for "good enough" and continue to push boundaries, no matter how many obstacles they encounter along the way. And to the mentors, the friends, and the believers who have stood by me who didn't just show me the ropes but challenged me to aim higher, to stretch beyond what I thought was possible, and to never settle for average. Your unwavering support has been a guiding light, especially in moments when self-doubt threatened to take over. You've taught me that excellence is not about achieving perfection, but about having the courage to keep improving and pushing forward, even when the path isn't clear. Your belief in me has been a constant source of inspiration, and because of you, I've learned to embrace challenges not as barriers, but as opportunities for growth.

To all of you who have shaped this journey, thank you for being part of my story.

Contents

Contents

Contents

Foreword

In an era where software runs nearly every aspect of our lives, the quality of that software has never mattered more. And yet, quality doesn't happen by accident it's engineered, tested, and refined by those who dare to challenge assumptions, break systems, and ask better questions. Quality Assurance professionals are no longer gatekeepers at the end of the pipeline; they are collaborators, risk managers, and champions of the user experience.

Mastering Software Testing arrives at a time when the QA field is undergoing a profound transformation. Automation is now table stakes, release cycles are shorter, and the expectation for flawless user experiences is at an all-time high. But tools and frameworks alone aren't enough what we need is a solid foundation of principles, critical thinking, and a commitment to continuous improvement.

Devarsh Shah brings a rare combination of practitioner insight, teaching clarity, and deep respect for the QA craft. This book doesn't just tell you how to test it shows you how to think like a tester. From foundational concepts to advanced strategies, each chapter is grounded in real-world relevance.

Whether you're an aspiring tester seeking direction, a developer aiming to understand QA better, or a senior engineer looking to sharpen your edge, this book will meet you where you are and take you further.

Preface

Software testing has evolved from being an afterthought to becoming a discipline that directly impacts business success, user trust, and technological innovation. When I started my career, testing was often misunderstood as "just clicking buttons." Over the years, I've seen it transform into a powerful practice that shapes software quality, delivery pipelines, and customer experience.

This book is my attempt to consolidate years of hands-on experience, research, mentoring, and failures into one cohesive resource for anyone passionate about quality. Whether you're a beginner or a senior QA looking to expand your toolkit this guide is for you.

Let this not just be a book you read, let it be a mindset you adopt.

Acknowledgements

The journey of writing this book would not have been possible without the steadfast support and encouragement from several people who have played pivotal roles in both my personal and professional life. First and foremost, I extend my deepest gratitude to my family. Your unwavering belief in me, your boundless patience, and your constant encouragement through every stage of this journey have been the foundation on which this book was built. You have been my anchor, my strength, and my source of motivation. To my colleagues and students thank you for challenging me, for the insightful conversations, and for sharing your wisdom and ideas. Every day in your company has pushed me to refine my thoughts and become a better thinker, teacher, and practitioner. Your passion for learning and growth has continuously inspired me to push the boundaries of my own knowledge. A sincere and heartfelt thank you goes to all my mentors. You have not only sharpened my thinking but have also helped me to develop a deeper understanding of the subject. Your guidance, wisdom, and constructive criticism have shaped my approach to both life and work. Every piece of advice and every lesson shared has left a lasting imprint on my journey. I would like to extend a special note of appreciation to **Dr. Unnati Shah** and the entire team at **Unnati's Physiotherapy Clinic**. Your constant support, unrelenting patience, and faith in me throughout this endeavor have been invaluable. This book is not just my own it is a reflection of the collective support, guidance, and inspiration I have received from all of you.

Prologue

I remember the first time I broke a feature in production by accident, of course. I was new, excited, and testing was barely part of the process. The lesson was harsh, but it was also clear: quality can't be assumed; it must be earned.

That moment marked the beginning of my journey into software testing not as a backup plan or supporting role, but as a core discipline. Since then, I've worked across teams, domains, and technologies, learning that the essence of testing isn't about finding bugs it's about building trust.

This book is the result of that journey. It brings together everything I wish I had known starting out, and everything I've learned mentoring others. You'll find practical techniques, industry best practices, war stories, and maybe even a few uncomfortable truths. But more than that, you'll find a mindset one that sees quality not as a checkbox, but as a responsibility.

Mastering Software Testing is not just about doing testing better it's about thinking differently. If you're ready to go beyond scripts and checklists, to ask the hard questions, and to lead with quality, then this book is for you.

Let's get started.

— Devarsh Shah

About The Author

Devarsh Shah is an inspiring leader, visionary co-founder, and a respected voice in the field of Quality Assurance and Engineering. He is known for combining the science of testing with the art of impact-driven innovation. With years of experience across QA disciplines, **Devarsh** has consistently driven transformation in organizations, enabling them to deliver secure, scalable, and robust software solutions. He began his journey as a passionate QA analyst and grew into a mentor for over **500+ professionals**, guiding them to achieve certifications, industry placements, and technical excellence. His influence extends beyond just training, he has **published national-level research papers**, spoken at conferences, and shaped policy-driven QA strategies in mission-critical sectors like healthcare and automation. As a **certified Six Sigma expert**, **Project Manager**, and **Scrum Practitioner**, **Devarsh** blends agile thinking with lean execution. His expertise spans across manual testing, automation frameworks, DevOps pipelines, machine learning integration in alert systems, and more. He is also a **content creator and public educator**, using social media and digital platforms to simplify complex testing concepts and raise awareness about the evolving landscape of quality engineering.

"I don't just test software. I test limits of possibility, patience, and potential."

Whether it's building from scratch or scaling automation across enterprise teams, **Devarsh** brings heart, hustle, and high standards to everything he does and forward-thinking Quality Assurance leader who believes that testing isn't just about finding bugs it's about building trust. From mentoring over 500+ budding QA professionals to publishing nationally recognized research papers, **Devarsh** has carved his journey with relentless dedication, curiosity, and innovation. As a co-founder in the healthcare and engineering domain, his work bridges mission-critical systems with world-class software practices. He holds multiple industry certifications including ISTQB, Six Sigma, and Project Management, and specializes in crafting robust test strategies, architecting automation frameworks, and coaching agile QA teams. **Devarsh** is also a tech content creator, a believer in AI-enhanced alert systems, and an advocate of continuous learning.

“Quality isn't a phase. It's a philosophy.”

Quality is not a checkbox at the end of a process it’s the mindset that shapes every decision from the very beginning. When treated as a phase, quality becomes reactive, often limited to inspection or correction after flaws emerge. But when embraced as a philosophy, it becomes proactive and deeply ingrained in culture, craftsmanship, and commitment.

Organizations and individuals who adopt quality as a core belief build trust, consistency, and long-term value. It influences how we design, communicate, and deliver ensuring excellence is not an exception, but the standard. In this light, quality is not a temporary effort, it’s a way of thinking and working that defines our identity and shapes our legacy.

ONE

INTRODUCTION TO SOFTWARE TESTING

What is Software Testing?

Software testing is the practice of evaluating and verifying that a software product or application performs as intended. It is a critical component of the Software Development Life Cycle (SDLC) that ensures quality, reliability, security, and user satisfaction. Testing helps uncover defects and bugs, improves performance, ensures compliance, and prevents failures in production environments.

At its core, software testing is not only about finding bugs. It is about building confidence in the system, validating its behavior, and ensuring that the user experience is smooth and error-free.

"The goal of software testing isn't to confirm that your code works it's to uncover where and how it fails."

Why is Testing Important?

- **Quality Assurance**: Prevents the release of faulty software.
- **Cost Efficiency**: Early bug detection reduces the cost of defect resolution.
- **Customer Satisfaction**: A seamless, error-free product leads to higher user retention and satisfaction.
- **Risk Mitigation**: Helps in identifying vulnerabilities and reducing risk exposure.

Historical Background

Software testing began in the 1950s when computing was primarily for academic and government research. Early testing was manual, slow, and lacked structure. As software evolved, so did the need for structured testing practices, leading to methodologies like Waterfall, V-Model, and later Agile and DevOps.

Evolution Timeline

Decade

Key Milestones

1950s

Manual debugging, no formal testing processes

1970s
Introduction of structured programming, unit testing
1990s
Waterfall & V-Model testing, emergence of QA teams
2000s
Agile methodology introduces iterative testing
2010s
Test Automation becomes mainstream, Selenium, JUnit
2020s
DevOps and CI/CD pipelines, AI-driven test automation

Key Objectives of Testing

1. **Verification and Validation**
    a. Are we building the product, right? (Verification)
    b. Are we building the right product? (Validation)
2. **Detecting Defects**
    a. Prevent defects from reaching the user.
3. **Gaining Confidence in Product**
    a. Prove the software can be deployed to production safely.
4. **Compliance and Documentation**
    a. Ensure software meets industry standards (e.g., ISO, GDPR).

Scope of Software Testing

- **Web Applications**
- **Mobile Applications**
- **APIs and Web Services**
- **Cloud and SaaS Platforms**
- **Embedded Systems and IoT Devices**

Role of a QA Professional

QA professionals not only test software but also:

- Participate in requirements analysis
- Design test plans and cases
- Execute manual and automated tests
- Track bugs and work with developers to resolve them
- Validate product releases
- Ensure continuous quality improvement

Real-World Example: NASA Mars Climate Orbiter Failure

NASA's Mars Climate Orbiter crashed in 1999 because one team used metric units and another used imperial units. The software didn't convert them properly, leading to the loss of a $125 million mission, a textbook example of failed integration testing.

Tools Used in Testing (Introductory Glimpse)

- **Manual Testing Tools**: TestLink, Zephyr
- **Automation Tools**: Selenium, Cypress, Playwright
- **Bug Tracking**: Jira, Bugzilla

Summary

Software testing is the foundation of product quality and user trust. It saves money, prevents errors, and ensures a smooth experience for end users. Whether you're testing a login page or a satellite launch program, the role of QA is invaluable.

Software testing is a systematic process that evaluates and verifies that a software product or application performs as expected. The goal is to identify bugs, ensure quality, and validate that the product meets both business and technical requirements.

"Software testing is not about proving your code works, it's about proving it doesn't break."

Software testing goes far beyond showing that a program runs under ideal conditions. Its true purpose lies in uncovering hidden faults, edge cases, and unexpected behaviors. It's not about celebrating that the code works when everything goes right it's about challenging it to fail and making sure it doesn't.

Great testing simulates real-world unpredictability. It asks, "What if the user does this?" or "What happens when the system is under pressure?" This mindset ensures reliability, resilience, and user trust. Testing, then, is not a final checkmark but a continuous process of strengthening the code by attempting to break it before your users ever get the chance.

TWO

IMPORTANCE OF SOFTWARE TESTING

Why Testing is Crucial in the Software Development Life Cycle

Software testing plays a mission-critical role in the SDLC. It helps detect bugs early, ensures compliance with functional and non-functional requirements, improves user experience, and significantly reduces the risk and cost of failure post-deployment.

Key Benefits of Software Testing

1. Early Detection of Bugs

The earlier a bug is found in the development process, the cheaper and easier it is to fix. Studies show that a defect found during production can cost up to 100x more than one found during requirement analysis or development.

2. Ensuring Software Reliability

Users expect systems to work without fail. Testing ensures the product functions correctly under expected and unexpected scenarios.

3. Improved Security

Security testing identifies vulnerabilities such as SQL injection, insecure data storage, and broken authentication mechanisms. This is critical for domains such as banking, healthcare, and e-commerce.

4. Compliance with Industry Standards

Industries such as healthcare (HIPAA), finance (SOX), and aviation (DO-178C) require strict testing to meet regulatory compliance. Testing ensures legal safety and audit readiness.

5. Customer Satisfaction and Retention

A well-tested application provides a seamless user experience, builds trust, and encourages customer loyalty.

Cost of Poor Quality (COPQ)

If a defect reaches production:

- Cost of patching the issue
- Customer dissatisfaction and churn
- Brand image loss
- Potential legal ramifications

"The bitterness of poor quality remains long after the sweetness of meeting the schedule is forgotten."

Types of Failures Caused by Poor Testing

Real-World Case Studies:

- **Starbucks (2015)**: POS system crashes due to software deployment issue led to store closures across the US and Canada.
- **Nissan Recall**: Over 1 million vehicles recalled due to airbag sensor software issues.
- **China Airlines Airbus A300 Crash**: Caused by a software bug leading to 264 fatalities.
- **Knight Capital Group (2012)**: A bug in trading software resulted in a $440 million loss in under an hour.

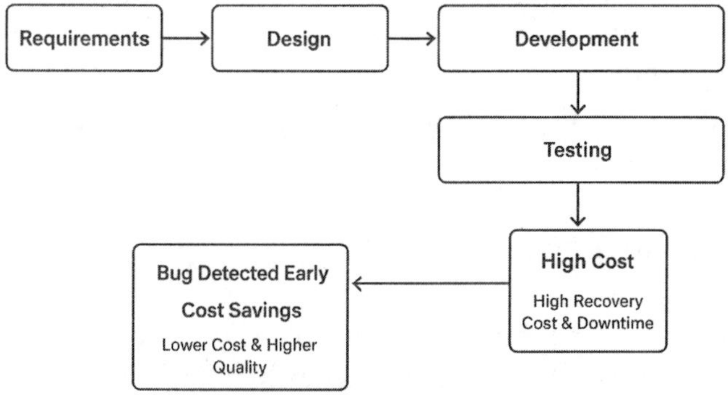

Software Development Life Cycle

Testing vs Quality Assurance

Feature	Testing	Quality Assurance
Focus	Product	Process
Purpose	Detect bugs	Prevent bugs
Activities	Execution, reporting	Process improvement, audits
Involvement Stage	Post-development	Throughout SDLC

Metrics to Justify Importance of Testing

- **Defect Density**: Defects per 1000 lines of code (KLOC)
- **Test Coverage**: Percentage of code/features tested
- **Mean Time to Detect (MTTD)** and **Mean Time to Repair (MTTR)**
- **Customer Reported Defects**: Measure of missed bugs

Summary

Testing is not a luxury it is a necessity. It supports the product's success by reducing errors, improving user experience, ensuring compliance, and building a reliable digital environment. Organizations that prioritize testing outperform those that treat it as an afterthought. Testing ensures error detection, reliability, security, and compliance. Real-world failures (e.g., Nissan recalls, Starbucks outages, bank errors) underscore the need for robust QA.

"Quality is never an accident, it is always the result of intelligent effort."

Quality doesn't happen by chance. It is the outcome of thoughtful design, deliberate choices, and consistent discipline. When we say "quality is never an accident," we recognize that excellence is not stumbled upon it's engineered through planning, skill, and attention to detail.

Behind every high-quality product, service, or system is a series of intelligent efforts decisions made with purpose, processes refined with care, and standards upheld with integrity. Whether in software development, craftsmanship, or leadership, quality is achieved when people choose to do things the right way, not the easy way.

It's not a stroke of luck. It's the reward for doing things with intention.

THREE

TYPES OF SOFTWARE TESTING

Software testing is not a one-size-fits-all activity. Based on objectives, timing, system architecture, and performance requirements, software testing can be broadly categorized into three main types:

Functional Testing

Functional testing verifies that each function of the software operates in conformance with the specified requirements. This type of testing answers the question: "Does the software do what it is supposed to do?"

Key Techniques:

- **Unit Testing** – Validates individual code modules.
- **Integration Testing** – Checks the interaction between integrated units or components.

- **System Testing** – End-to-end validation of the software as a whole.
- **User Acceptance Testing (UAT)** – Ensures the product meets business needs and is ready for production.

Example:

Testing whether the login feature successfully accepts valid credentials and restricts unauthorized access.

Non-Functional Testing

Non-functional testing assesses how the system performs under specific conditions rather than what it does. It includes performance, usability, and reliability aspects.

Key Techniques:

- **Performance Testing** – Checks system responsiveness and stability.
- **Load Testing** – Simulates expected user traffic.
- **Stress Testing** – Evaluates system behavior under extreme conditions.
- **Usability Testing** – Verifies user-friendliness.
- **Security Testing** – Identifies vulnerabilities.

Example:

Testing how a banking website performs when 1000 users log in simultaneously.

Maintenance Testing

Maintenance testing involves validating changes in an application post-deployment. This ensures that new features or fixes do not negatively affect the existing system.

Key Techniques:

- **Regression Testing** – Ensures new changes haven't broken existing functionality.
- **Retesting** – Re-executes test cases that previously failed.
- **Confirmation Testing** – Confirms if bug fixes work as intended.

Example:

After fixing a bug in the cart feature, the entire checkout workflow is re-tested to ensure stability.

Comparison Table

Type	**Goal**	**Example Scenario**
Functional Testing	Verifies actions/output	Login feature validation
Non-Functional	Evaluates performance/reliability	Load handling for 10,000 users
Maintenance	Tests changes after deployment	Verify new build doesn't break old features

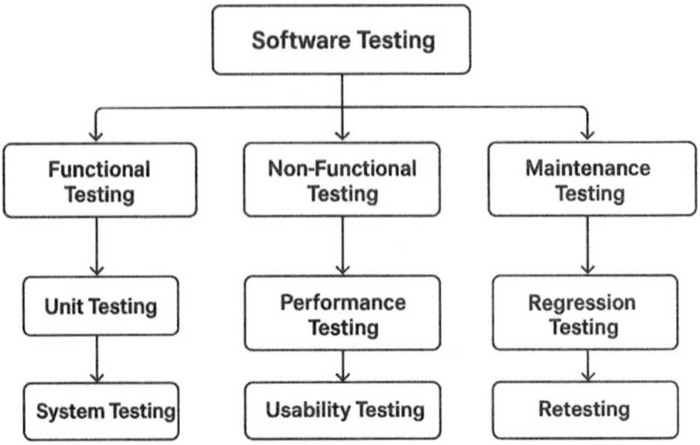

Different Testing Types

Summary

Each testing type plays a unique role in ensuring the completeness and quality of the software. Functional testing checks correctness, non-functional evaluates experience and performance, while maintenance testing guards ongoing product stability.

- **Functional**: Validates features.
- **Non-Functional**: Tests performance, usability.
- **Maintenance**: Involves regression and retesting.

"Testing types are like pillars together they uphold the temple of quality."

In the world of software development, quality doesn't stand on a single foundation it rests on many. Each type of testing, from unit and integration to performance and security, acts as a pillar, supporting the structure of a reliable and robust product.

Just as a temple needs all its columns to stand strong, a system requires multiple layers of testing to ensure it performs well, remains secure, and delivers a seamless user experience. No single test can guarantee quality alone; it's the collective strength of diverse testing methods that uphold the entire framework.

Together, these testing types form the architecture of confidence, ensuring that the final product isn't just functional, but dependable.

FOUR

QA TESTING TRIAD

Software testing encompasses several domains, each with unique goals, methods, and impact. This chapter takes a deeper dive into the **three essential categories** of testing: Functional, Non-Functional, and Maintenance Testing along with advanced examples, metrics, and diagrams.

Functional Testing (In Depth)

Functional testing ensures that the application behaves according to the business and technical specifications. It focuses on verifying *what* the system does.

Key Techniques:

1. **Unit Testing** – Focuses on individual code units or methods.
2. **Integration Testing** – Tests interfaces and data flow between components.
3. **System Testing** – End-to-end system functionality.
4. **Sanity & Smoke Testing** – Initial, basic checks before deeper testing.

5. **User Acceptance Testing (UAT)** – Verifies system readiness by the business/user team.

Tools for Functional Testing:

- Selenium
- Test Complete
- QTP/UFT

Example:
A hotel booking app is tested to ensure a user can:

- Search available hotels
- Select a room
- Complete the payment process successfully

Metrics:

- **Requirement Coverage (%)** = (Covered Requirements / Total Requirements) × 100
- **Test Case Effectiveness (%)** = (Defects Detected / Total Defects Introduced) × 100

Non-Functional Testing (In Depth)
Non-functional testing checks *how* well the system performs under various conditions such as load, stress, security, and usability.
Key Areas:

1. **Performance Testing** – Response times, throughput, and resource usage.

2. **Load Testing** – Application stability under expected load.
3. **Stress Testing** – System behavior beyond load limits.
4. **Security Testing** – Authentication, data encryption, and access control.
5. **Compatibility Testing** – Cross-browser, cross-platform behavior.
6. **Usability Testing** – User-friendliness, intuitiveness.

Performance Metrics:

Metric	Definition
Response Time	Time taken for system to respond
Throughput	Number of transactions per second
CPU Usage	System resource utilization

Security Checklist:

- HTTPS enabled
- Session timeout
- SQL Injection protection
- Password encryption

Maintenance Testing (In Depth)

Maintenance testing ensures that modifications whether bug fixes or enhancements do not adversely impact the existing system.

Key Activities:

1. **Regression Testing** – Ensures existing functionalities still work.
2. **Retesting** – Confirms that specific defects have been resolved.
3. **Impact Analysis** – Understands what areas are affected by a change.

Example:

A new promo code feature is added to an e-commerce checkout page. Regression tests are executed for cart, payment, and order confirmation flows to ensure overall stability.

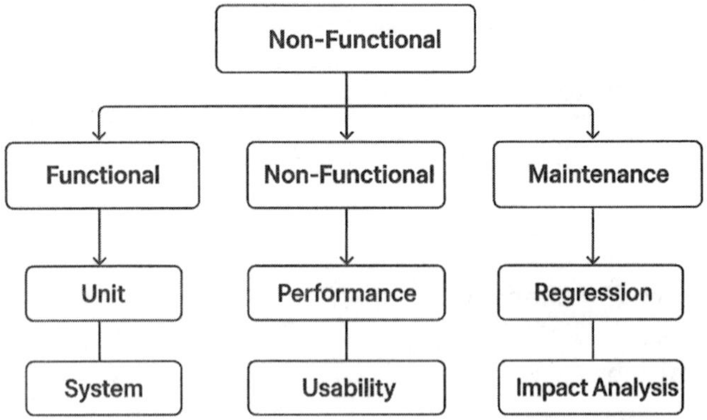

Comparison Diagram

Summary Table

Category	Focus Area	Tools	Example Use Case
Functional	Business Logic & UI Behavior	Selenium, TestComplete	Booking flow on travel app
Non-Functional	Performance, UX, Security	JMeter, OWASP ZAP	Stress test on banking login
Maintenance	Post-release validation	Selenium, Postman	Retest after a bug fix or hotfix

Summary

These three pillars, functional, non-functional, and maintenance testing ensure total software assurance. Together, they confirm that the application not only meets expectations but also performs efficiently and evolves reliably over time.

Functional Testing

Unit, integration, system, and acceptance testing.

Non-Functional Testing

Performance, load, stress, usability, and security testing.

Maintenance Testing

Regression, retesting, confirmation testing.

"A stable product is not one without bugs, but one that evolves without collapsing."

A stable product isn't defined by the absence of bugs it's defined by its ability to grow, adapt, and improve without falling apart. In reality, no software is ever truly bug-free. What sets a strong product apart is its resilience: the ability to handle change gracefully, whether through new features, updates, or scaling demands.

Stability means maintaining integrity under pressure. It means developers can introduce improvements without triggering chaos, and users can rely on the product to function consistently even as it evolves. This kind of stability is built on solid architecture, thoughtful design, and a commitment to continuous testing.

True stability isn't perfection it's controlled, confident progress.

FIVE

TESTING STRATEGIES

Testing strategies define the approach and guidelines followed to achieve testing goals. A well-designed strategy ensures comprehensive test coverage, risk minimization, and optimal use of time and resources.

Types of Testing Strategies

1. Unit Testing Strategy

- Focuses on verifying individual functions or methods.
- Performed by developers during the coding phase.
- Often automated for efficiency.
- Tools: JUnit, NUnit, PyTest

2. Top-Down Integration Testing

- Starts testing from the top-level modules and integrates down.
- Stubs are used to simulate lower modules.

- Best when high-level logic is ready first.

3. Bottom-Up Integration Testing

- Begins with testing low-level modules first and integrates upward.
- Drivers are used to simulate upper modules.
- Ideal for testing foundational utility functions first.

4. Big Bang Integration Testing

- All modules are integrated and tested simultaneously.
- Fast setup but challenging to isolate defects.
- High risk due to lack of progressive validation.

5. Incremental Testing

- Modules are tested as they are integrated, either top-down or bottom-up.
- Allows early defect detection.

6. Risk-Based Testing

- Testing is prioritized based on the risk of failure and impact.
- Focus is placed on mission-critical features.
- Applied in banking, aviation, and healthcare sectors.

7. Exploratory Testing

- Simultaneous learning and test design by testers.
- Ideal for early development phases or when documentation is limited.

- High creativity and intuition required.

Strategy Selection Criteria

- **Project Scope and Size**
- **Risk Tolerance**
- **Team Skillset**
- **Available Tools and Resources**
- **Delivery Deadlines**

V-Model (Validation & Verification Model)

The V-Model is an extension of the waterfall model where each development stage has a corresponding testing activity. It promotes early test planning and design.

V - Model

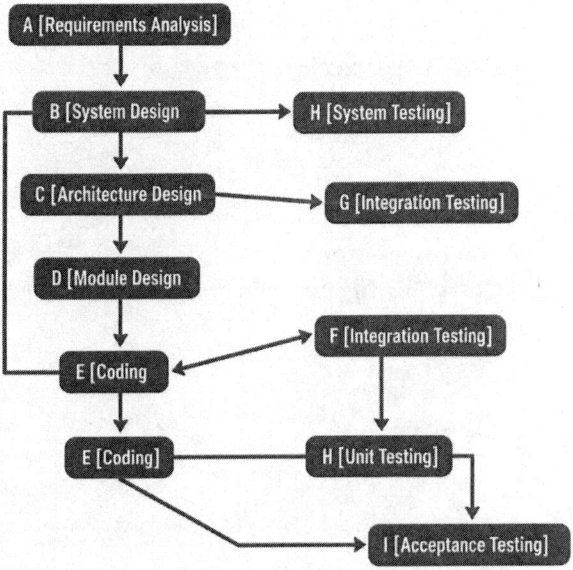

Left Side (Development Phases)

- Requirements
- System Design
- Architecture
- Module Design
- Coding

Right Side (Testing Phases)

- Acceptance Testing
- System Testing
- Integration Testing
- Unit Testing

Real-World Application Example:

A financial trading platform may use:

- **Risk-Based Testing** for transaction modules.
- **Top-Down Integration** to test business logic flows.
- **Exploratory Testing** to validate dynamic UI behavior under different user roles.

Summary Table

Strategy	Best For	Risk Level	Tool Examples
Unit Testing	Individual code logic	Low	JUnit, PyTest
Top-Down Integration	High-level business logic	Medium	Custom stubs
Bottom-Up Integration	Low-level utility validation	Medium	Drivers, Mocks
Big Bang Testing	End-to-end check	High	Jenkins pipelines
Risk-Based Testing	High-priority business areas	Variable	Jira + Risk Matrix
Exploratory Testing	Unstructured systems	Variable	Session-based logging

Summary

Choosing the right strategy is foundational to successful test planning. Whether driven by risk, schedule, or system design, a good strategy balances efficiency with thoroughness. Unit testing, top-down, bottom-up, big bang, risk-based, and exploratory testing strategies with suggested V-model flowchart for visualization.

A Breakthrough

"In the V-Model, testing is not an afterthought it's an equal partner of development."

Didn't Understand that, well read it again!

"A bad strategy wastes effort. A good one amplifies impact."

SIX

SOFTWARE TESTING LIFE CYCLE (STLC)

The Software Testing Life Cycle (STLC) is a series of well-defined phases in testing to ensure software quality and delivery. Unlike traditional development, STLC introduces structure and accountability to each phase of testing.

Each phase in the STLC is associated with deliverables, entry/exit criteria, and stakeholder involvement.

STLC Phases:

1. Requirement Analysis

- Understand what needs to be tested.
- Analyze requirements from both functional and non-functional perspectives.
- Identify testable and non-testable areas.

Deliverables: Requirement Traceability Matrix (RTM)

2. Test Planning

- Create a roadmap for testing.
- Define scope, test objectives, effort estimation, and scheduling.
- Identify risks and mitigation strategies.

Deliverables: Test Plan Document, Risk Management Plan

3. Test Case Development

- Design test scenarios, test cases, and test data.
- Peer reviews and approval for completeness and accuracy.

Deliverables: Test Case Repository, Test Data Sheets

4. Test Environment Setup

- Prepare hardware, software, network, and configurations.
- Mirror the production environment as closely as possible.

Deliverables: Configured Test Environment, Environment Setup Checklist

5. Test Execution

- Execute test cases manually or via automation.
- Report and log defects in bug tracking tools.
- Conduct retesting and regression.

Deliverables: Test Execution Reports, Defect Logs

6. Test Closure

- Evaluate exit criteria.
- Assess test metrics, coverage, defect density, and lessons learned.
- Archive test artifacts for compliance.

Deliverables: Test Summary Report, Lessons Learned Document

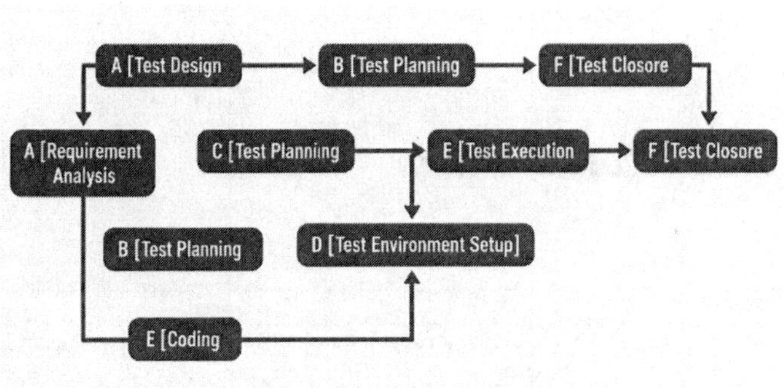

Software Testing Life Cycle

STLC Metrics to Track

Metric	Description
Test Case Coverage (%)	% of total planned test cases executed
Defect Detection Rate	Defects found / Total executed test cases
Defect Leakage Rate	% of defects found post-release
Requirement Coverage	Linked test cases per requirement

Entry and Exit Criteria

Phase	Entry Criteria	Exit Criteria
Requirement Analysis	Signed-off requirements document	RTM prepared; ambiguity clarified
Test Planning	Requirements analyzed	Test strategy and plan signed off
Test Case Development	Approved test plan	All test cases and data reviewed
Test Environment Setup	System design available, tools ready	Environment configured and verified
Test Execution	Test cases ready, environment stable	All cycles complete, defects retested
Test Closure	Testing completed	Closure report submitted and approved

Summary

STLC provides structure, accountability, and standardization in QA practices. It integrates testing into every phase of delivery and ensures consistent progress monitoring through documentation and metrics.

Phases of STLC

Requirement Analysis → Test Planning → Test Case Development → Test Environment Setup → Test Execution → Test Closure.

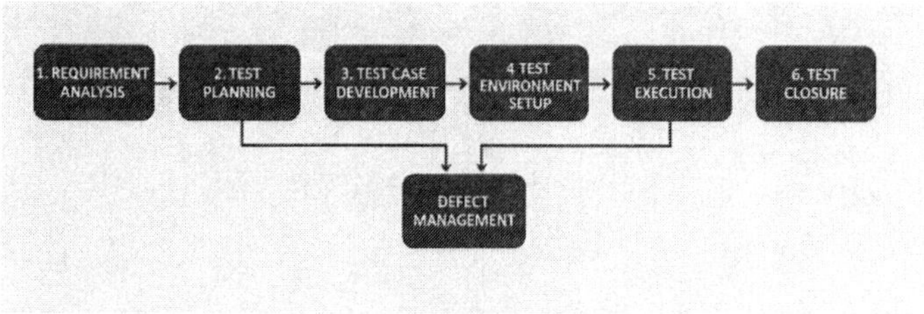

STLC PHASES

"A successful test cycle doesn't end with defect closure it ends with learning, improvement, and trust."

A successful test cycle is not measured solely by the number of defects closed it's measured by what the team learns, how the process improves, and the trust it builds in the product. Closing bugs is a milestone, but it's not the destination.

Each test cycle is an opportunity to understand the system better, uncover patterns, strengthen test strategies, and refine communication between teams. The insights gained help prevent future issues, speed up development, and enhance user satisfaction.

Ultimately, effective testing cultivates trust not just in the product, but within the team. Trust that the system works, that problems are found early, and that quality is a shared goal, not just a checklist.

SEVEN

AUTOMATION VS. MANUAL TESTING

Automation and manual testing are two fundamental approaches in software testing. Choosing between them or using them together depends on project requirements, timelines, team expertise, and cost considerations.

What is Automation Testing?

Automation testing uses specialized tools and scripts to execute test cases, verify outcomes, and report results without human intervention. It is especially beneficial for regression, performance, and repetitive test execution.

Key Benefits:

- Faster test execution
- High repeatability
- Better accuracy and consistency
- Supports CI/CD pipelines
- Ideal for large-scale applications

Popular Tools:

- Selenium WebDriver (Web UI)
- Cypress (End-to-end testing)
- JUnit, TestNG (Java)
- Playwright (Modern browser automation)
- Robot Framework (Keyword-driven)

Use Cases:

- Regression testing after frequent code changes
- Smoke testing in continuous delivery
- Load testing large datasets or API calls

What is Manual Testing?

Manual testing is the process of executing test cases by a human tester without automation tools. It relies on the tester's intuition, adaptability, and creativity.

Key Benefits:

- Ideal for exploratory, usability, and UI testing
- Helps uncover unexpected issues not covered in scripts
- Great for ad-hoc and one-time tests

Use Cases:

- User Acceptance Testing (UAT)
- Exploratory Testing
- Tests with frequently changing UI
- Domain validation where judgment is crucial

Feature Comparison

Attribute	Manual Testing	Automation Testing
Execution Speed	Slow	Fast
Human Error	Possible	Eliminated (if well-scripted)
Setup Time	Minimal	High (initial script development)
Flexibility	High (adaptive)	Rigid (fixed scripts)
Reusability	Low	High
Best For	UI, Ad-hoc, Usability Testing	Regression, Performance, CI/CD
Learning Curve	Low	Moderate to High

Automation ROI Metrics

Metric	Description
Automation Coverage	% of test cases automated
Script Maintenance Cost	Time to update scripts post code change
Test Execution Time	Average duration to execute test cycles
Defects Found	Bugs caught by automation scripts

Real-World Example:

A SaaS platform with daily deployments uses:

- **Manual testing** for UI consistency across browsers and user experience feedback

- **Automation testing** for regression, smoke, and login flows using Selenium and Jenkins

Hybrid Testing Approach

Most organizations use a hybrid approach that combines manual and automated testing for maximum efficiency. The idea is to automate repetitive and critical flows while retaining manual effort for exploratory and design-focused scenarios.

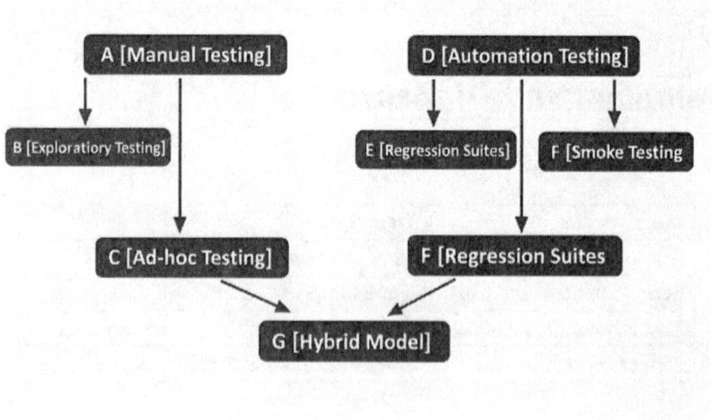

Hybrid Model

Summary

Both manual and automation testing are essential. Manual testing brings creativity, domain insight, and flexibility, while automation ensures speed, scalability, and efficiency. A balanced strategy makes QA more effective.

"Automate the predictable. Humanize the exceptional."

Criteria	**Manual Testing**	**Automation Testing**
Speed	Slow	Fast
Accuracy	Human-dependent	High
Reusability	Low	High
Cost	High (long-term)	Lower over time

Tools: Selenium, Cypress, TestNG, Playwright

"Machines run the race, but humans read the map, testing needs both to reach the finish line."

In modern software testing, machines may run the race, but it's humans who read the map. Automation brings speed, precision, and repeatability but without human judgment, context, and adaptability, the testing journey can go off course.

Automated tests are essential for covering repetitive tasks and ensuring consistency at scale. But it's human testers who interpret results, explore edge cases, question assumptions, and align testing with real-world user behavior. They bring creativity, critical thinking, and a sense of direction that no script can replicate.

To truly reach the finish line delivering a high-quality, reliable product testing must be a collaboration. Machines handle the pace, humans handle the purpose. Together, they drive quality forward.

EIGHT

SOFTWARE TESTING TECHNIQUES

Testing techniques are structured methods for designing and selecting test cases. They help maximize test coverage while ensuring efficiency and clarity. These techniques are broadly classified into three major categories:

Black Box Testing Techniques

Black box techniques focus on the functionality of the software without knowing the internal code structure. The tester validates the output based on inputs and expected behavior.

1. Equivalence Partitioning (EP)

Divides input data into valid and invalid partitions. Only one test case per partition is required.

Example: If age input is valid between 18–60, test cases could be: 17 (invalid), 18 (valid), 60 (valid), 61 (invalid).

2. Boundary Value Analysis (BVA)

Tests boundaries of input ranges, where most bugs occur.

Example: For input 1–100, test: 0, 1, 2, 99, 100, 101.

3. Decision Table Testing

Used for systems with complex business logic. Combines inputs and expected outcomes into a tabular format.

Condition A	Condition B	Action
TRUE	FALSE	X
FALSE	TRUE	Y

4. State Transition Testing

Tests software behavior under various input states.

Example:

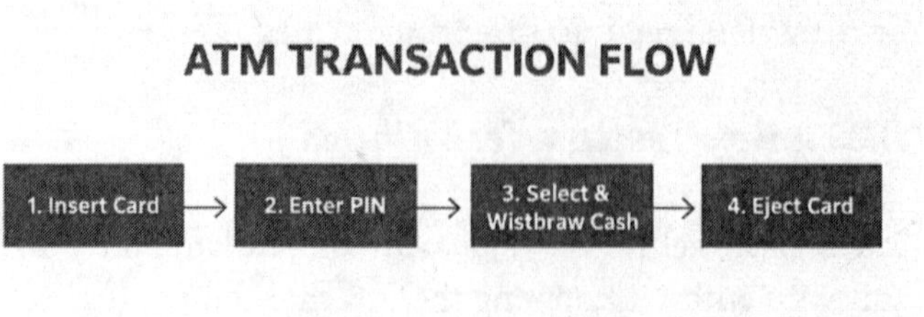

ATM Transaction Flow

5. Error Guessing

Relies on tester experience to guess problematic areas.

Example: Entering special characters into form fields that expect numbers.

White Box Testing Techniques

White box testing requires knowledge of internal code structure. It's generally done by developers.

1. Statement Coverage

Ensures every executable line of code is tested.

2. Branch Coverage

Ensures every decision (if-else) is tested.

3. Condition Coverage

Ensures each Boolean sub-expression is tested independently.

Example:

For the code:

```
if (A > B) and (C == D):
perform_action()
```

Branch coverage tests both true/false outcomes, while condition coverage tests A > B and C == D separately.

Experience-Based Testing Techniques

These are informal techniques relying on the tester's intuition, domain knowledge, and exploratory skills.

1. Exploratory Testing

Simultaneous learning, test design, and execution. Highly flexible and effective for short cycles.

2. Ad-hoc Testing

Unstructured testing without documentation. Best used in early or very late stages.

3. Checklist-Based Testing

Testers use a predefined list of common error-prone areas to validate.

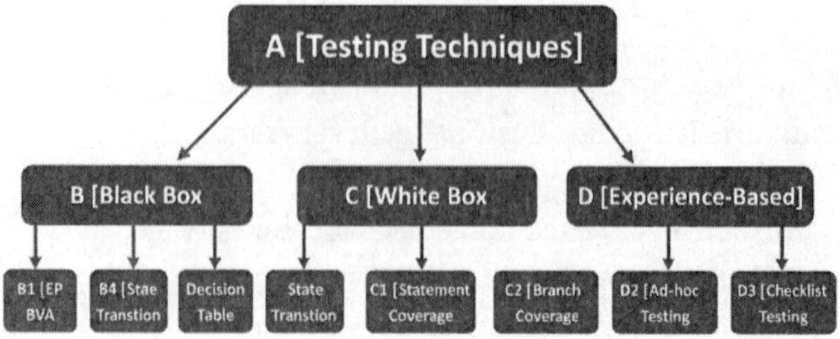

Classification of Testing Techniques

Summary Table

Category	Technique	Best For
Black Box	EP, BVA, State Testing	Functional validation
White Box	Branch, Statement	Code-level validation
Experience-Based	Exploratory, Ad-hoc	Quick insights & unexpected behaviors

Summary

Mastering testing techniques enables QA professionals to design high-impact test cases, reduce redundancy, and boost overall effectiveness. A great tester knows when to apply which technique not all bugs are found by tools, some are found by thought.

Black Box Testing Techniques

Black box testing focuses on evaluating the functionality of the software without any knowledge of the internal code structure or logic. Testers concentrate on inputs and expected outputs, ensuring the system behaves as intended.

- **Equivalence Partitioning (EP):** This technique divides input data into valid and invalid partitions or classes. Test cases are then designed to cover each partition, reducing the total number of tests while maintaining coverage. The assumption is that all values within a class will be treated similarly by the software.
- **Boundary Value Analysis (BVA):** Since errors often occur at the edges of input ranges, BVA targets the values at and around the boundaries of input domains. Test cases are created to check these critical edge points, including minimum, maximum, just below, and just above boundary values.
- **Decision Table Testing:** This method is useful when the software behaves differently based on various combinations of inputs or conditions. A decision table lists inputs, rules, and corresponding outcomes, helping to ensure that all possible scenarios are tested.
- **State Transition Testing:** Applied when a system changes its behavior based on previous actions or inputs, this technique uses states, transitions, and events to model and verify different possible sequences of operations.

White Box Testing Techniques

White box testing involves examining the internal structure, logic, and code of the software. Testers need programming knowledge to design effective test cases.

- **Statement Coverage:** Ensures that every executable statement in the code is run at least once during testing. It helps to confirm that no lines of code are skipped.
- **Branch Coverage:** Tests all possible branches or decision points (e.g., if-else conditions) in the code. This ensures that every possible path has been taken at least once.
- **Condition Coverage**: Focuses on evaluating each individual condition in a decision. It verifies that every Boolean sub-expression evaluates to both true and false at least once.

Experience-Based Testing Techniques

These techniques rely on the tester's intuition, knowledge, and previous experience with similar systems or defects.

- **Exploratory Testing**: Conducted without predefined test cases, this approach allows testers to explore the application dynamically. Testers learn about the system as they test, designing and executing tests on the fly.
- **Ad-Hoc Testing:** A less structured approach where tests are performed without formal planning or documentation. It relies heavily on the tester's understanding of the application and is often used to quickly identify obvious defects

"Techniques turn intuition into insight."

Intuition is the starting point an instinct, a gut feeling that something needs attention. But in testing and development, intuition alone isn't enough. Techniques are what transform that raw instinct into actionable insight.

Whether it's through structured exploratory testing, root cause analysis, or data-driven debugging, techniques give form and direction to our intuition. They help us validate assumptions, uncover hidden issues, and communicate findings with clarity.

In this way, techniques don't replace human intuition they elevate it. They convert vague suspicion into verified understanding, turning hunches into evidence and uncertainty into confidence. This is how quality is not only sensed but proven.

NINE

WRITING TEST SCENARIOS & TEST CASES

Test scenarios and test cases are the core of structured testing practices. They help ensure full coverage of software functionality, make testing repeatable, and improve communication among QA, development, and business teams.

What is a Test Scenario?

A test scenario is a high-level description of what needs to be tested. It defines the goal of a test without detailing exact steps.

Characteristics:

- Focuses on end-user workflows or business use cases

- Easy to understand for stakeholders
- Often written before detailed test cases

Example:

Scenario: Verify that a user can reset their password using the "Forgot Password" link.

What is a Test Case?

A test case is a detailed set of conditions under which a tester determines whether a software application is working correctly. It includes the input, action, expected result, and actual result.

Standard Test Case Format:

Field	**Description**
Test Case ID	Unique identifier (e.g., TC_001)
Title/Name	Brief description of the test case
Preconditions	Setup or conditions required before executing
Test Steps	Step-by-step instructions
Test Data	Input values
Expected Result	What should happen
Actual Result	Observed outcome (filled during execution)
Status	Pass/Fail
Priority/Severity	Business/technical impact
Comments	Notes, screenshots, or additional observations

Example Test Case

Test Case ID	Title	Preconditions	Steps	Expected Result
TC_01	Login with valid credentials	User registered	1. Open login page. 2. Enter username and password. 3. Click Login.	User is redirected to dashboard

Tools for Writing & Managing Test Cases

- **TestRail**
- **Zephyr**
- **QTest**
- **Xray (Jira Plugin)**
- **Spreadsheets (for small teams/startups)**

Best Practices for Writing Effective Test Cases

- Keep steps concise and repeatable
- Avoid technical jargon if business users will review
- Ensure traceability to requirements via RTM
- Prioritize high-risk scenarios first
- Group test cases into logical suites
- Peer-review test cases for accuracy

Traceability Matrix (RTM)

A Requirements Traceability Matrix links test cases to corresponding requirements. It ensures complete coverage and simplifies auditing.

Requirement ID	Requirement Description	Test Case ID(s)
REQ_01	Users must be able to log in	TC_01, TC_02
REQ_02	Users must reset passwords	TC_03, TC_04

Test Case Metrics

Metric	Description
Test Case Execution %	(Executed / Total) × 100
Pass Rate %	(Passed / Executed) × 100
Defect Detection Rate	(Defects Found / Executed Tests) × 100

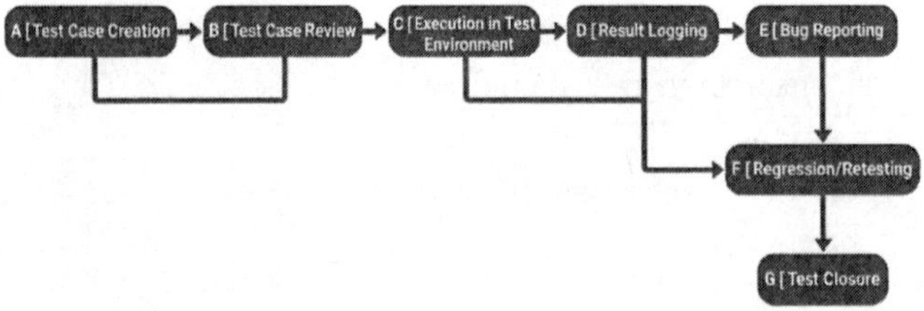

Summary

Test scenarios give us direction. Test cases give us execution precision. Together, they serve as the foundation for reliable, repeatable, and traceable software testing.

"Test cases are the bridge between requirements and reality."

Test Case ID	Description	Input Data	Expected Result
TC_01	Login with valid credentials	user/test, pass	Redirect to dashboard

Tip: Use test management tools like TestRail or Zephyr.

"A well-written test case is not just a checklist, it's a blueprint for uncovering the truth in code."

A well-written test case is far more than a series of steps to follow it's a purposeful design that seeks clarity, accuracy, and truth. While checklists confirm what's expected, a thoughtfully crafted test case goes deeper: it challenges assumptions, probes for hidden flaws, and ensures the code behaves as intended in real-world conditions.

Good test cases are structured, but never rigid. They guide testers not only through actions, but through intent why we're testing, what we expect, and what we risk if we're wrong. In this sense, they become blueprints for uncovering the truth buried within complexity.

When test cases are written with care and curiosity, they don't just validate code they reveal it.

TEN

BUG AND DEFECT MANAGEMENT

Bug and defect management is the backbone of quality assurance, providing a structured approach to identifying, recording, tracking, and resolving software anomalies. Proper defect handling ensures robust software delivery and enhances collaboration across QA, development, and management teams.

Defining Bugs and Defects

A **defect** (also known as a **bug**) is an issue in software that leads to incorrect or unexpected behavior. These may result from coding errors, miscommunication in requirements, integration problems, or infrastructure conflicts.

Key Definitions

Term	Description
Error	A human mistake in coding, configuration, or requirements
Defect	A flaw that causes deviation from expected behavior
Bug	Informal term used interchangeably with defect
Failure	Execution that results in unexpected or incorrect output

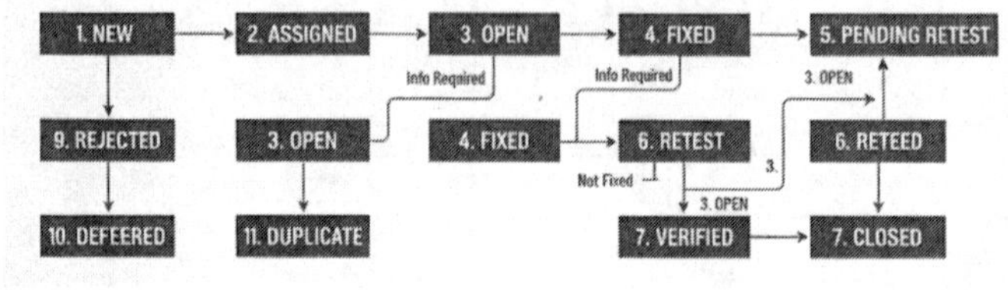

Defect Life Cycle

Severity vs Priority

Category	Definition	Example
Severity	Impact on system functionality	App crashes during login (High Severity)
Priority	Urgency of fixing the defect	Logo misaligned on homepage (Low Severity, High Priority)

Bug Report Essentials

Field	Description
Bug ID	Unique reference number
Title	Short summary of the bug
Steps to Reproduce	Clear instructions to replicate the issue
Actual vs Expected	What happened vs. what should have happened
Environment	OS, browser, version, hardware
Attachments	Screenshots, logs, videos
Severity & Priority	Technical and business impact levels

Tools for Defect Tracking

- **Jira**
- **Bugzilla**
- **Azure DevOps**
- **MantisBT**

Case Study Example

- In a financial app, A failed transaction bug is **Critical Severity, High Priority**. A color inconsistency in a theme switcher is **Low Severity, Low Priority**.

"Finding a bug is science, managing it is strategy, great testers master both."

Finding a bug is a scientific process observation, hypothesis, experimentation, and evidence. It demands attention to detail, a deep understanding of the system, and the curiosity to explore beyond the obvious. But discovering a defect is only half the battle.

Managing that bug prioritizing it, communicating its impact, and ensuring it's resolved efficiently is a matter of strategy. It involves collaboration, risk assessment, and a clear understanding of business goals and user expectations.

Great testers excel at both. They are part scientist, part strategist skilled in uncovering flaws, and equally skilled in navigating the complex journey from discovery to resolution. That balance is what elevates testing from a task to a craft.

ELEVEN

AGILE AND DEVOPS TESTING

Agile and DevOps have transformed how software is built, tested, and released. Traditional QA processes had to evolve to fit the rapid, iterative, and collaborative workflows of modern development.

Agile Testing: A Continuous Quality Mindset

Agile testing is integrated early and continuously within the development lifecycle. Rather than being a separate phase, testing becomes a collaborative effort among developers, testers, and product owners.

Agile Principles That Impact Testing:

- Individuals and interactions over processes and tools
- Working software over comprehensive documentation
- Customer collaboration over contract negotiation
- Responding to change over following a plan

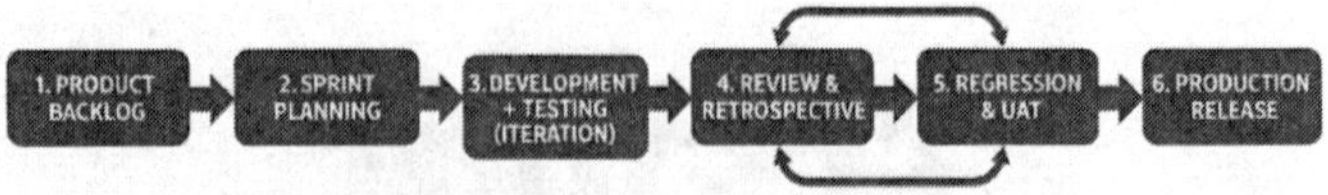

Agile Testing Lifecycle

Agile Testing Quadrants

Quadrant	Type of Test	Tools	Purpose
Q1	Unit & Component Tests	JUnit, NUnit	Technology-facing (support dev)
Q2	Functional & Story Tests	Selenium, Postman	Business-facing (support dev)
Q3	Exploratory & Usability Testing	Session-based testing	Business-facing (critique product)
Q4	Performance & Security Testing	JMeter, OWASP ZAP	Technology-facing (critique product)

DevOps Testing: Automation Across the Pipeline

DevOps bridges development and operations by emphasizing CI/CD (Continuous Integration/Continuous Delivery). QA is embedded into the delivery pipeline with automated checks at every stage.

DevOps Pipeline

DevOps Tools Landscape

Phase	Tools
CI/CD	Jenkins, GitLab CI/CD
Versioning	Git, GitHub, Bitbucket
Testing	Selenium, JUnit, Postman
Monitoring	New Relic, Datadog, Grafana

DevOps Testing Types

- **Smoke Tests**: Basic validation post-deployment
- **Regression Suites**: Automated via CI/CD triggers
- **Infrastructure Testing**: Validate IaC (e.g., Terraform)
- **Monitoring & Logging Tests**: Detect production anomalies

Real-World Example

A fintech app deploys 3 times daily. Each build runs:

- 200+ automated UI/API tests
- Static code checks via SonarQube

- Canary deployments for real-time monitoring

"In Agile and DevOps, testing isn't a phase, it's a pulse that keeps the delivery alive."

In traditional models, testing was seen as a phase a separate stage that came after building was done. But in Agile and DevOps, that mindset no longer fits. Testing isn't something you wait for; it's something that happens continuously. It becomes the pulse that keeps the rhythm of delivery alive.

With rapid iterations, frequent deployments, and continuous integration, testing must flow alongside development not behind it. It provides constant feedback, detects issues early, and ensures that every heartbeat of the pipeline is strong and stable.

In this fast-moving environment, testing isn't just a task. It's a lifeline. And without it, the system stops being agile it simply starts breaking.

TWELVE

WEB APPLICATION TESTING

Web applications require thorough testing due to their widespread use, public accessibility, and frequent updates. This chapter outlines the different facets of web testing, including functionality, UI, compatibility, and security aspects.

Key Areas in Web Testing

Web applications are accessed by a wide range of users across different devices, platforms, and browsers. To ensure a seamless, secure, and high-performing user experience, various areas of testing must be thoroughly covered. Below are the core aspects of web testing:

1. Functionality Testing

Functionality testing ensures that every feature of the web application operates according to its specifications. The goal is to validate that the core functions behave as intended under different conditions.

Key components include:

- **Links and Navigation:** Testing all internal and external hyperlinks to ensure they are functional and lead to the correct destinations.
- **Forms and Input Fields:** Validating form inputs, including text fields, checkboxes, radio buttons, and drop-downs, to ensure proper data capture and submission.
- **Error Handling:** Ensuring appropriate error messages appear when invalid inputs are submitted or when unexpected actions occur.
- **Cookies and Sessions:** Verifying that cookies store the correct data and sessions maintain user state securely throughout the user journey.
- **Database Interactions:** Testing CRUD operations (Create, Read, Update, Delete) to confirm data is accurately processed and stored.

2. UI/UX Testing (User Interface and User Experience Testing)

This area focuses on assessing the visual appearance and overall user interaction with the application. A well-designed interface enhances user satisfaction and usability.

Key aspects include:

- **Visual Elements:** Ensuring consistent use of colours, fonts, icons, and branding elements throughout the application.
- **Layout Consistency:** Verifying that all elements are properly aligned and displayed, even on varying screen

sizes.

- **Responsiveness:** Testing how the interface adapts to different screen resolutions (mobile, tablet, desktop).
- **Interactive Elements:** Checking buttons, sliders, modals, and navigation menus for proper responsiveness and feedback.
- **Accessibility:** Ensuring the application is usable by individuals with disabilities, including support for screen readers and keyboard navigation.

3. Compatibility Testing

Given the diversity in web browsers, devices, and operating systems, compatibility testing is crucial to ensure consistent behavior and appearance.

Testing is performed across:

- **Multiple Browsers:** Verifying compatibility with popular browsers like Chrome, Firefox, Safari, Edge, and Opera.
- **Different Devices:** Testing on various devices including smartphones, tablets, laptops, and desktops.
- **Operating Systems:** Ensuring functionality on Windows, macOS, Linux, Android, and iOS.
- **Network Environments:** Testing how the application behaves under different internet speeds and conditions.

4. Performance Testing

Performance testing evaluates how well the application performs under various conditions, particularly when handling large volumes of traffic or data.

Key metrics include:

- **Page Load Speed:** Measuring how quickly pages and resources load under normal and peak conditions.
- **Response Time:** Assessing how fast the application responds to user interactions and server requests.
- **Stress Testing:** Determining the application's breaking point by pushing it beyond normal operating conditions.
- **Scalability:** Evaluating how well the system adapts to increasing user demand or data processing needs.

5. Security Testing

With the increasing number of web-based threats, security testing has become essential to protect user data and ensure system integrity.

Focus areas include:

- **Authentication:** Verifying that only authorized users can access certain parts of the application.
- **Authorization:** Ensuring users have access only to features and data they are permitted to use.
- **Data Encryption:** Checking if sensitive data is encrypted both in transit and at rest.
- **Session Management:** Ensuring that user sessions are properly maintained and terminated after inactivity or logout.
- **Vulnerability Testing:** Identifying and mitigating common security flaws such as SQL injection, cross-site scripting (XSS), and cross-site request forgery (CSRF).

Tools

- Selenium, Cypress

- Postman, REST Assured
- JMeter, Lighthouse
- OWASP ZAP, Burp Suite
- BrowserStack, Sauce Labs

Real-World Example

Testing an online marketplace to ensure:

- Mobile and desktop experience parity
- Secure transactions via HTTPS
- Quick search and product filtering under 2 seconds

"Web testing is more than clicks and pages, it's ensuring every user journey ends in trust, not trouble."

Web testing is not just about verifying clicks or checking if pages load correctly. It's about safeguarding the entire user journey, making sure each interaction feels smooth, secure, and reliable. Every user visit is a story, and web testing ensures that story ends with satisfaction not frustration.

From performance and functionality to security and accessibility, web testing covers all bases to create a seamless experience. When done well, it builds trust turning casual visitors into loyal users and one-time transactions into lasting relationships.

In essence, web testing is the guardian of reputation, ensuring technology serves people, not the other way around.

THIRTEEN

STATIC TESTING AND REVIEWS

Static testing involves the evaluation of software work products without executing the code. It focuses on documentation, design, and code review to catch defects early in the Software Development Life Cycle (SDLC).

Key Techniques in Static Testing

1. Reviews

Manual inspection of documents or code for accuracy and completeness.

Review Type	**Participants**	**Objective**
Informal Review	Peers	General feedback
Walkthrough	Author + Team	Share understanding and gather input
Technical Review	Developers/Testers	Evaluate for correctness and quality
Inspection	Moderator, QA, Recorder	Formal defect identification

2. Static Code Analysis

Automated tools scan source code for violations of coding standards, complexity, and potential security issues.

Popular Tools: SonarQube, ESLint, Checkstyle, Pylint

Benefits of Static Testing

- Detects issues early (before code execution)
- Improves code readability and maintainability
- Enhances collaboration and team learning
- Reduces cost of late-stage defect fixes

Real-World Example

A retail software firm incorporated SonarQube into its CI pipeline. It identified critical security issues (hardcoded passwords, missing validation) before they reached production saving thousands in potential damage.

"Static testing sees the cracks before the foundation is poured, it's quality built at the blueprint stage."

Static testing is like inspecting the blueprint before the foundation is poured. It identifies cracks, inconsistencies, and potential flaws early long before the code is executed or the system is built. By catching issues at this stage, static testing saves time, effort, and cost down the line.

This proactive approach ensures that quality is designed into the product from the very beginning, rather than patched on later. It's a crucial step that strengthens the entire development process, building a solid foundation upon which reliable, maintainable software can stand.

In short, static testing is quality's first line of defense, shaping success from the start.

FOURTEEN

PERFORMANCE AND STRESS TESTING

Performance testing ensures that a system behaves as expected under various conditions. It verifies speed, scalability, and stability of critical factors for customer satisfaction.

Major Types of Performance Testing

Type	Purpose	Example
Load Testing	Measure response under expected load	1,000 users browsing simultaneously
Stress Testing	Push system beyond its limits	10x traffic spike
Spike Testing	Rapid increase/decrease in load	Sudden flash sale
Soak Testing	Long duration under normal load	48-hour streaming performance
Volume Testing	Evaluate performance with large data sets	Uploading 1M records in one batch

Metrics

- Response Time
- Throughput
- Error Rate
- Resource Utilization (CPU, RAM, DB)

Tools

- Apache JMeter
- LoadRunner
- BlazeMeter
- Gatling
- K6.io

Case Study

A video conferencing app experienced user lag during peak hours. After spike testing with 10,000+ virtual users, the QA team discovered a bottleneck in session memory allocation. Patching this improved stability by 35%.

Using Real-Time Data in JMeter

Apache JMeter is a powerful open-source tool for performance testing. One of its practical capabilities is the ability to use real-time or dynamic data during test execution. This means instead of hardcoding values like usernames, passwords, or search queries, JMeter can fetch and use live or updated data from external sources. This makes the test more realistic and closer to how real users interact with a system.

Why Use Real-Time Data in JMeter?

In real-world applications, user inputs are rarely the same. For example:

- Different users log in at different times
- Search queries vary from person to person
- Form submissions contain unique data

If your test uses only static data, it might not reflect real usage scenarios. Using real-time or dynamic data improves the accuracy, coverage, and reliability of performance testing.

Common Ways to Use Real-Time Data in JMeter

1. CSV Data Set Config

One of the easiest ways to bring real-time data into JMeter is by using the CSV Data Set Config element. This allows JMeter to read input values from a .csv file (like Excel) during test execution.

Example Use Cases:

- Logging in with different user credentials
- Submitting forms with unique values
- Performing searches with multiple keywords

Steps:

1. Create a CSV file (e.g., users.csv) with sample data like usernames and passwords.

2. Add a CSV Data Set Config element in your test plan.

3. Set the file path and assign variable names to each column.

4. Use those variable names in your HTTP Request or Form fields.

Metrics

- Response Time
- Throughput
- Error Rate
- Resource Utilization (CPU, RAM, DB)

Tools

- Apache JMeter
- LoadRunner
- BlazeMeter
- Gatling
- K6.io

Case Study

A video conferencing app experienced user lag during peak hours. After spike testing with 10,000+ virtual users, the QA team discovered a bottleneck in session memory allocation. Patching this improved stability by 35%.

Using Real-Time Data in JMeter

Apache JMeter is a powerful open-source tool for performance testing. One of its practical capabilities is the ability to use real-time or dynamic data during test execution. This means instead of hardcoding values like usernames, passwords, or search queries, JMeter can fetch and use live or updated data from external sources. This makes the test more realistic and closer to how real users interact with a system.

Why Use Real-Time Data in JMeter?

In real-world applications, user inputs are rarely the same. For example:

- Different users log in at different times
- Search queries vary from person to person
- Form submissions contain unique data

If your test uses only static data, it might not reflect real usage scenarios. Using real-time or dynamic data improves the accuracy, coverage, and reliability of performance testing.

Common Ways to Use Real-Time Data in JMeter

1. CSV Data Set Config

One of the easiest ways to bring real-time data into JMeter is by using the CSV Data Set Config element. This allows JMeter to read input values from a .csv file (like Excel) during test execution.

Example Use Cases:

- Logging in with different user credentials
- Submitting forms with unique values
- Performing searches with multiple keywords

Steps:

1. Create a CSV file (e.g., users.csv) with sample data like usernames and passwords.

2. Add a CSV Data Set Config element in your test plan.

3. Set the file path and assign variable names to each column.

4. Use those variable names in your HTTP Request or Form fields.

File content: users.csv	In your test:
username,password	${username} and ${password}
user1,pass1	
user2,pass2	

Each virtual user will use a different row from the CSV during the test.

2. Using Functions and Variables

JMeter supports built-in functions like:

- __Random() – to generate random numbers
- __UUID() – to generate unique IDs
- __time() – to fetch the current timestamp

These can be used to simulate real-time user activity.

User ID: user_${__Random(1000,9999)}

Timestamp: ${__time(YMDHMS)}

This ensures that each request is unique, just like in a live scenario.

3. Fetching Data from a Live API

In some advanced cases, you might need to fetch data from an API before making the actual test request. JMeter allows this by chaining requests.

Example Workflow:

1. Use one HTTP Request to call a REST API that returns live data (e.g., product IDs).
2. Extract the needed value using **JSON Extractor** or **Regular Expression Extractor**.
3. Use that extracted value in the next request.

This helps you simulate a real user journey with updated or live system data.

4. Using Database Data

You can also connect JMeter to a live database using **JDBC Connection Configuration**. This allows your test to query real-time data directly from the backend.

Steps:

1. Add a JDBC Connection Configuration element with your DB details.
2. Add a JDBC Request to fetch data (e.g., select usernames).
3. Use the result in further HTTP requests.

This approach is useful for:

- Verifying backend data consistency
- Using production-like test data
- Simulating data-driven user flows

Benefits of Using Real-Time Data in JMeter

- **More realistic scenarios** – Simulates how real users interact with your application.
- **Avoids caching issues** – Unique requests reduce the risk of results being cached.
- **Better coverage** – Tests cover a wider range of input combinations.

- **Improved test reliability** – Detects edge cases and hidden issues.

Incorporating real-time data in your JMeter test plans transforms basic scripts into powerful simulations of real-world usage. Whether it's through CSV files, random functions, APIs, or databases, using dynamic data improves test accuracy and ensures your application can handle diverse user behaviours.

"Performance testing reveals how fast stress testing reveals and how far both show that how strong your system truly is."

Performance testing shows how fast your system can operate under normal conditions, measuring responsiveness and stability. Stress testing goes further it pushes the system to its limits and beyond, revealing how much load it can endure before breaking.

Together, they provide a comprehensive picture of your system's strength and resilience. Performance testing tells you what your system can handle comfortably, while stress testing uncovers its breaking points and helps prepare for unexpected challenges.

By combining both, you understand not just how fast your system runs, but how far it can go and how strong it really is when the pressure's on.

FIFTEEN

TEST DOCUMENTATION

Test documentation is the structured output of QA efforts and acts as both a testing guide and historical record. It ensures transparency, traceability, and regulatory compliance.

Key Types of Test Documents

Document Type	Purpose
Test Plan	Scope, objectives, schedule, roles, and risks
Test Scenarios	High-level functionality validation
Test Cases	Step-by-step instructions to test features
Test Data	Input values and conditions for testing
Defect Reports	Detailed logs of bugs with steps, severity, priority
Traceability Matrix	Mapping of requirements to test cases
Summary Report	Test outcome, pass/fail rate, lessons learned

Tools

- TestRail
- Zephyr (Jira plugin)
- Xray
- Microsoft Excel (manual teams)

Best Practice

Maintain version control, peer review documentation, and regularly update test cases when features change.

"Test documentation turns fleeting tests into lasting knowledge because quality fades without a written trail."

Test documentation transforms momentary testing efforts into a permanent source of wisdom. Without a written record, valuable insights, decisions, and lessons risk being forgotten or overlooked, causing quality to fade over time.

By capturing test cases, results, and observations, documentation creates a clear trail that teams can follow, review, and build upon. It ensures consistency, facilitates knowledge transfer, and supports continuous improvement.

In essence, test documentation is the memory of quality preserving what was learned so that future testing is smarter, faster, and more effective.

SIXTEEN

QA AS A CAREER PATH

The QA domain offers vast opportunities from functional testers to test architects, with evolving roles across manual, automation, DevOps, and AI testing.

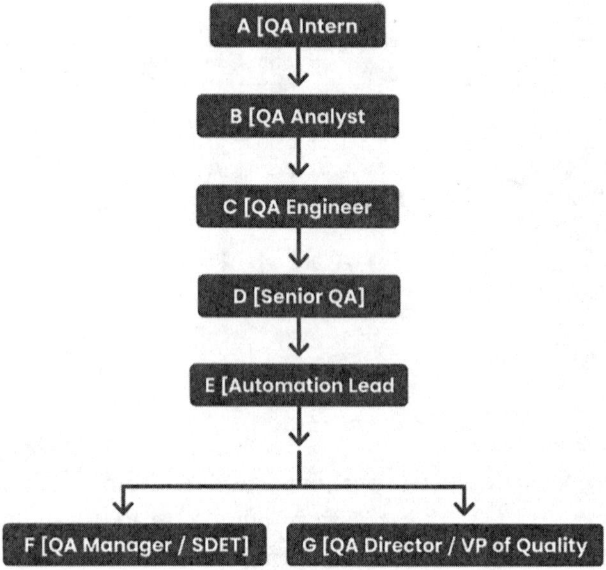

QA Role Evolution

Required Skills

- Test design & documentation
- Selenium, Cypress, Playwright
- API testing (Postman, REST Assured)
- Agile & Scrum knowledge
- CI/CD: Jenkins, GitHub Actions
- Performance: JMeter, K6

Certifications

Cert	Description
ISTQB Foundation	Core QA knowledge
Agile Tester	QA in agile environments
Selenium Certification	Automation scripting with Selenium
CSTE	Certified Software Test Engineer (QAI)

Industry Trends

- Shift-left testing and QAOps
- AI/ML in defect prediction
- Rise of no-code test automation

Salary Insights (Approx.)

Role	India (INR/year)	US (USD/year)
QA Analyst	₹4–6 LPA	$60k–80k
Automation QA	₹8–15 LPA	$90k–120k
QA Manager	₹18–25 LPA	$130k–160k

Career Tip

Upskill continuously, tools change, but core QA principles (like defect prevention, test coverage, risk-based testing) remain timeless.

"QA isn't just a job it's a mindset of excellence."

Quality Assurance isn't merely a role or a set of tasks it's a mindset that drives every action toward excellence. It's about attention to detail, relentless curiosity, and a commitment to delivering the best possible outcome.

QA professionals don't just find defects; they advocate for users, challenge assumptions, and inspire continuous improvement. This mindset shapes how teams collaborate, how processes evolve, and ultimately, how products succeed.

In QA, excellence isn't optional it's the standard.

SEVENTEEN

INTERVIEW QUESTIONS & ANSWERS

This chapter presents a curated set of interview questions and model answers tailored for QA professionals from freshers to advanced roles such as SDETs, QA Leads, and Automation Architects.

Beginner-Level QA Interview Questions

Q1. What is the difference between verification and validation?

- **Answer:**
    - *Verification* ensures that the product is built correctly (meets specifications).
    - *Validation* ensures that the correct product is built (meets user needs).

Q2. What are the different levels of software testing?

- **Answer:** Unit Testing, Integration Testing, System Testing, Acceptance Testing.

Q3. What is the purpose of a test case?

- **Answer:** A test case provides step-by-step instructions, input data, and expected results to validate a specific software function.

Q4. What are functional vs. non-functional testing?

- **Answer:**
    - *Functional testing* validates business logic.
    - *Non-functional testing* checks performance, security, usability, etc.

Intermediate-Level QA Interview Questions

Q5. Explain the defect life cycle.

- **Answer:** States include New → Assigned → Open → Fixed → Retest → Verified → Closed (or Reopened, Rejected, Deferred).

Q6. What is regression testing?

- **Answer:** Re-running tests after changes to ensure unchanged functionality still works.

Q7. What's the difference between smoke and sanity testing?

- **Answer:**
    - *Smoke testing:* Basic build verification.
    - *Sanity testing:* Focused testing after a fix or minor change.

Q8. How do you prioritize test cases?

- **Answer:** Based on risk, business impact, and user-critical features. High-risk areas are tested first.

Advanced-Level & Automation QA Questions

Q9. What frameworks have you used in automation testing?

- **Answer:** Selenium with TestNG/JUnit, Cucumber (BDD), Page Object Model (POM), Cypress, Robot Framework.

Q10. How do you integrate test automation in CI/CD?

- **Answer:** Automation scripts are triggered post-build in Jenkins/GitLab CI using tools like Maven, Gradle, or shell scripts.

Q11. What is parameterization in automation?

- **Answer:** Feeding different data sets into test scripts to run the same test with multiple inputs.

Q12. Describe how you handle dynamic elements in Selenium.

- **Answer:** Use XPath with wildcards, wait conditions, or JavaScriptExecutor for dynamic elements.

Q13. What are the challenges in test automation?

- **Answer:**
    - High initial setup cost
    - Test script maintenance
    - Test environment reliability
    - Handling UI changes

Behavioral & Situational QA Questions

Q14. How do you handle missed defects in production?

- **Answer:** Conduct RCA (Root Cause Analysis), update test cases, improve peer reviews, and introduce automated checks if needed.

Q15. Have you ever disagreed with a developer? How did you resolve it?

- **Answer:** Maintain a collaborative tone, bring data/evidence, and focus on the product quality over personal opinions.

Q16. What do you do when requirements are unclear?

- **Answer:** Communicate with stakeholders, use exploratory testing, create assumption-based test cases, and validate post-clarification.

Additional QA / Automation Interview Questions & Answers

Q17. What is the difference between severity and priority of a defect?

Answer:

- **Severity** refers to how serious or critical the defect is in terms of system behaviour (e.g. crash, data loss).
- **Priority** indicates how soon the defect should be fixed (based on business need).
  A defect might be high severity but low priority (e.g. rare edge case), or low severity but high priority (e.g. cosmetic issue on main page).

Q18. What is testability and why is it important?

Answer:
Testability is how easy it is to design and execute tests for a given software component. It is important because high testability helps testers detect issues sooner, reduces effort in writing tests, and improves the overall quality of testing. Good testability arises from modular design, clear interfaces, observability (logs, debugging), and minimal dependencies.

Q19. How do you select which test cases to automate?

Answer:

You prioritize automating test cases that are:

- Repetitive and time-consuming
- Stable (i.e. not changing often)
- High risk or high business impact
- Good candidates for regression tests
- Data-driven or suitable for parameterization

Avoid automating tests that require frequent human judgment (e.g. usability) or are highly volatile.

Q20. What is *parallel test execution*, and how is it useful?

Answer:

Parallel test execution means running multiple test cases or suites simultaneously (on different machines, threads, or containers)

Benefits include:

- Reducing total execution time
- Faster feedback in CI/CD pipelines
- Better utilization of hardware / cloud resources

  Challenges include managing dependencies, data isolation, and environment setup.

Q21. What is the *Page Object Model (POM)* in test automation?

Answer:

Page Object Model is a design pattern in which each webpage (or UI screen) is represented by a class or object. That object encapsulates web element locators and methods to interact with that page (click, input, read).

Benefits:

- Reduces code duplication
- Improves readability and maintainability
- Changes to UI affect only the page object class, not all tests

Q22. Explain *hard assert* vs *soft assert* in test automation.

Answer:

- **Hard assert** immediately stops test execution when an assertion fails.
- **Soft assert** allows the test to continue executing further steps even if some verifications fail; then it reports all failures at the end.
  Soft asserts are useful when you want to check multiple conditions in a single run rather than halting at the first failure.

Q23. What is *headless browser testing*? Why use it?

Answer:

Headless browser testing is running browser automation without a visible GUI (Graphical User Interface). The browser operates in the background.

Advantages:

- Faster execution
- Less resource consumption
- Useful in CI/CD pipelines or servers without a display
  Popular headless browsers: Headless Chrome, Puppeteer, PhantomJS (older).

Q24. What is *service virtualization* and why is it needed in testing?

Answer:

Service virtualization is simulating (mocking) components or services that are not available, unreliable, or expensive (e.g. external APIs, third-party systems).
It is needed because:

- It allows testers to continue when dependent systems are not ready
- Ensures predictable responses for test cases
- Helps isolate the system under test and reduce external dependencies in automation

Q25. What is *continuous testing* in DevOps?

Answer:

Continuous testing is the practice of executing automated tests (unit, integration, API, UI) continuously through the delivery pipeline every time there is a code change.
Goals:

- To detect defects early
- To provide immediate feedback to developers
- To maintain high confidence in each deployment

Q26. How do you handle flaky or intermittent test failures?

Answer:

Approaches include:

- Adding retries with backoff (only for non-critical steps)
- Improving synchronization (explicit waits, polling)
- Isolating test data and environment so tests don't interfere
- Analyzing logs and failure patterns to find root causes

- Marking unstable tests and prioritizing their stabilization

Q27. What is *mutation testing*?

Answer:

Mutation testing involves deliberately introducing small changes ("mutations") to the code and checking whether existing test cases detect the introduced defects (i.e. tests fail). If tests don't fail, it indicates weak test coverage or insufficient assertions. It helps evaluate the effectiveness of your test suite.

Q28. How is *shift-left testing* different from traditional testing?

Answer:

In **traditional testing models**, much of the testing happens after development is complete (later in the cycle). In **shift-left testing**, testing begins earlier right from requirements, design or development phases. The idea is to find defects sooner, reduce cost of fixes, and integrate testing with development.

Q29. What are *test metrics* you would monitor in an automation project?

Answer:

Some useful metrics include:

- Test coverage (lines, branches, paths)
- Pass / fail rate
- Defect detection rate
- Execution time and test throughput
- Flakiness rate (percentage of intermittent failures)
- Automation ROI (time saved vs cost of maintenance)

Q30. What is *AI / self-healing tests* and how is it being used in QA today?

Answer:

Self-healing tests refer to automation frameworks that detect when a UI element locator fails, and automatically adapt or find alternate locators (using AI or heuristics).

This reduces the maintenance burden when UI changes occur. Some modern test tools incorporate AI to analyse patterns, suggest fixes, or auto-update tests

Q31. What is the difference between *test plan* and *test strategy*?

Answer:

- A **test strategy** outlines the overall approach, objectives, resources, and methods that will guide testing across the project. It's a high-level document.
- A **test plan** is more detailed and project-specific: it includes scope, schedule, test deliverables, test environment, resources, and responsibilities for a particular phase or release.

Q32. What is *API testing* and how is it different from UI testing?

Answer:

- **API testing** checks the application's backend services, endpoints, and data exchange (requests, responses, status codes, payloads) often using tools like Postman, REST Assured, etc.
- **UI testing** validates the user interface (buttons, layout, navigation). API testing is faster, more stable (less prone to UI changes), and helps detect issues deeper in the

application logic.

Q33. What are *TDD (Test-Driven Development)* and *BDD (Behaviour-Driven Development)*?

Answer:

- **TDD** is a development approach where you write tests before writing the actual code. You follow the cycle: write a failing test → implement code → refactor.
- **BDD** extends TDD with more emphasis on behaviour and readability, often using human-readable formats (e.g. Gherkin syntax in Cucumber). It encourages a common language between technical and non-technical stakeholders.

Q34. What is *code coverage*, and what types are used?

Answer:

Code coverage measures how much of your source code is executed when running tests. Types include:

- **Line (statement) coverage** – checks if each line was executed
- **Branch coverage** – checks if each branch (if/else) was executed
- **Condition coverage** – ensures each Boolean sub-expression was evaluated both true and false
- **Path coverage** – all possible execution paths are tested (can be very large)

Q35. What is *exception handling* in test automation and how do you handle exceptions?

Answer:

Exception handling ensures that unexpected errors don't

crash the test suite but are handled gracefully. You can:

- Use try-catch blocks around risky operations
- Log detailed information when exceptions occur
- Take screenshots if UI failure happens
- Fail a test gracefully and continue with next tests (if appropriate)
- Use retry logic for transient/temporary failures

Q36. What is *CI/CD pipeline* in relation to automation testing?

Answer:

CI/CD (Continuous Integration / Continuous Delivery) pipelines automate the steps from code commit to deployment. In testing:

- Automated tests are triggered after every build (CI)
- Failures block further steps and provide feedback
- Passing builds can be automatically deployed to staging or production (CD)

  This ensures faster feedback and safer releases.

Q37. What are *test suites*, *test sets*, and *test cycles* in testing?

Answer:

- **Test suite**: A collection of test cases grouped together (often by feature, module, or functionality).
- **Test set**: A subset of test cases selected for execution under specific conditions (e.g. nightly runs, smoke set).
- **Test cycle**: A planned run of a set of test cases during a test phase (e.g. regression cycle, sanity cycle).

Q38. What is *data-driven testing*?

Answer:

Data-driven testing separates test logic from test data. Test scripts are written to work with external data inputs (e.g. from Excel, CSV, databases). That way, you can run the same test logic with multiple data sets.

Q39. What is *keyword-driven testing* (or table-driven testing)?

Answer:

Keyword-driven testing uses a table (spreadsheet) of "keywords" or action names (like CLICK, INPUT, VERIFY) and arguments. The automation engine reads the table and performs actions based on keywords. It makes test scripts more maintainable and non-technical users can define tests.

Q40. What is *hybrid automation framework*?

Answer:

A hybrid framework combines features of multiple frameworks (e.g. modular, data-driven, keyword-driven, BDD) to get strengths of each. It's flexible and often tailored to project needs.

Q41. How would you test a login page both manually and via automation?

Answer (brief):

- **Manual**: Test valid credentials, invalid credentials, blank fields, locked accounts, error messages, password reset, UI look and feel.
- **Automation**: Create scripts for valid/invalid login, check redirection, handle cookies/session, test multiple users from data source, verify error messages, run across browsers.

Q42. How do you manage test environment issues (e.g. environment down, database not available) during execution?

Answer:

- Use environment health checks (before test run)
- Use fallback or mock services
- Alert the responsible team and abort tests
- Use retries or wait until environment is ready
- Maintain multiple environments (staging, dev, QA) to reduce single point of failure

Q43. What is log analysis and how can testers use logs?

Answer:

Log analysis involves inspecting server, application, or framework logs to find errors, performance bottlenecks, exceptions, or unexpected behavior. Testers use logs to debug failed tests, understand root cause, and trace execution flows beyond UI.

Q44. What is cross-API chain testing or end-to-end API testing?

Answer:

In real systems, multiple APIs interact (e.g. login API returns token → fetch user profile API → update settings API). Cross-API chain testing tests these flows end-to-end, ensuring integration and data consistency across calls.

Q45. What techniques would you use to test file upload/download features?

Answer:

- Verify supported file types, invalid file types
- Test upload of large files, small files, zero-size files
- Check download integrity (checksum, file contents)

- Test upload failure, retry, timeouts
- Validate UI feedback (progress bar, error message)
- Check security (e.g. uploading malicious files, file path traversal)

Q46. How do you test push notifications or real-time notifications (e.g. in web or mobile apps)?
Answer:

- Validate that notifications are delivered when expected (e.g. after event)
- Test content, timing, multiple recipients
- Simulate network delays or losses
- Test under high load
- Test permissions (opt-in / opt-out)
- Use mock services or test frameworks that support real-time protocols (WebSockets, MQTT)

Q47. What is test anchoring in automation?
Answer:
Test anchoring refers to techniques to keep tests stable despite UI changes, by using robust locators (e.g. IDs, data attributes), avoiding brittle XPath, using relative locators, and fallback locators. Anchors help tests survive minor UI updates.

Q48. How do you test email functionality (sending, receiving) as part of QA?
Answer:

- Use a test email account or mock mail server
- Validate that the mail is sent, subject, body, attachments
- Check for HTML vs plain text rendering
- Ensure links in email work correctly

- Test delays, retries, error handling, and spam filters
- Check logging and bounce handling

Q49. What is locust vs JMeter for load testing (or other alternatives)?
Answer:

- **JMeter** is Java-based, GUI available, supports complex scenarios, wide plugin ecosystem
- **Locust** is Python-based, lightweight, scriptable, better concurrency handling in code, good for real-code logic
- Others: Gatling (Scala), k6 (JavaScript), Artillery (JS) Choosing depends on team skills, scenario complexity, performance needs.

Q50. What is the future of QA / test automation (trends)?
Answer:

- AI-assisted or self-healing tests (locators adapt automatically)
- More no-code/low-code automation tools
- Shift-left / continuous testing integration
- Increased focus on non-functional testing (security, performance) baked in from early stages
- Observability and test analytics (using metrics, logs, dashboards)
- Integration of chaos engineering and fault injection into QA

Tips for QA Interview Success

- Learn the SDLC and STLC thoroughly.
- Practice whiteboard test case design.
- Know your resume projects deeply.
- Prepare to write test cases live.
- Have examples of bugs you caught and what they impacted.

"An interview tests not only your QA skills but your problem-solving mindset."

An interview is more than a quiz on QA techniques it's a window into how you approach challenges. It assesses your problem-solving mindset, creativity, and ability to think critically under pressure.

Employers want to see not just what you know, but how you apply knowledge, adapt to new scenarios, and communicate solutions. In QA, this mindset often matters just as much as technical skill.

Success in an interview comes from showcasing both your expertise and your strategic thinking.

EIGHTEEN

FINAL SUMMARY AND TAKEAWAYS

As you reach the conclusion of this book, it's important to reflect on the key principles, tools, and practices that define success in software testing. Whether you're starting your QA journey or elevating your role into leadership or automation, mastering core testing practices will always remain crucial.

Major Takeaways from This Book

Foundational Concepts

- Testing is more than bug detection it's about quality enablement.
- Understanding the SDLC and STLC lays the groundwork for all QA roles.
- Functional and non-functional testing work hand-in-hand to ensure a stable, usable, and scalable product.

Strategy and Technique

- Select the right testing strategy (risk-based, exploratory, regression) based on project goals.
- Black-box, white-box, and experience-based techniques each add different value.

Tool Mastery

- Automation tools (Selenium, Cypress, Postman) speed up testing but require robust frameworks.
- Performance and security tools (JMeter, OWASP ZAP) help ensure resilience.
- CI/CD integration elevates testing to a continuous activity in DevOps.

Documentation

- Writing effective test plans, cases, and reports ensures repeatability and transparency.
- Traceability via RTMs links requirements to validation.

Career Growth

- QA offers diverse career paths: Manual Tester, Automation QA, SDET, QA Lead, and QA Architect.
- Certifications (ISTQB, CSTE, Selenium) boost visibility and marketability.

Mindset Shift

- A good tester thinks like an end user.
- A great tester thinks like a hacker, developer, and product owner — all in one.

- Collaboration, curiosity, and continuous learning are the real skills that shape long-term growth.

What's Next?

- Practice: Join open-source QA projects, participate in bug bounty testing.
- Network: Engage in communities like Ministry of Testing, Stack Overflow, and LinkedIn QA forums.
- Upskill: Learn AI-powered testing, shift-left strategies, and visual testing for UI/UX assurance.

Final Thought

This book was written to equip you not just with information, but with inspiration to shape the next generation of quality-first software teams.

“Software without bugs isn’t a dream it’s a direction. And you, as a Quality Engineer, are the compass.”

Bug-free software isn’t an unattainable fantasy it’s a goal, a direction toward which every team strives. But getting there requires more than just code; it needs guidance, vigilance, and dedication. As a Quality Engineer, you are the compass guiding the development process.

You navigate through complexities, identify hidden risks, and help steer the project away from pitfalls. Your insights and actions keep the team aligned with the vision of delivering reliable, high-quality software.

In this journey, you don’t just test code you chart the course to excellence.

"Stay curious. Stay critical. Stay Quality Driven"

Quality starts with curiosity the eagerness to explore, question, and understand beyond the obvious. It thrives on critical thinking challenging assumptions, scrutinizing every detail, and never settling for "good enough." Together, these attitudes fuel a quality-driven mindset.

To stay quality driven is to commit to continuous learning, rigorous evaluation, and relentless improvement. It's the mindset that turns challenges into opportunities and delivers excellence consistently.

In the world of quality, these three principles aren't just advice they're a way of life.

Goodbye Mate!

As you close this book, remember that mastering quality assurance is not just about techniques or tools it's about embracing a mindset that drives excellence and innovation every single day. This journey you've embarked on is a commitment to leadership, continuous learning, and the courage to challenge the status quo. May these pages inspire you to see beyond the code, to build not just software, but trust and progress in everything you create.

"Quality isn't just built into software it's built into the mindset of those who dare to question it, refine it, and stand by it. True mastery in QA means leading with innovation and challenging the status quo because quality is not just maintained, it's revolutionized by those brave enough to redefine the future. Mastery isn't the end of a path, it's the beginning of seeing everything with sharper eyes and higher standards."

With passion for Quality and Innovation

Devarsh Shah